THE
QUILTER'S
BOOK *of* DAYS

CAROL ENDLER STERBENZ

PHOTOGRAPHY BY STEVEN MAYS

Martingale™
& COMPANY

CREDITS

President • Nancy J. Martin
CEO • Daniel J. Martin
Publisher • Jane Hamada
Editorial Director • Mary V. Green
Managing Editor • Tina Cook
Copy Editor • Allison A. Merrill
Design Director • Stan Green
Cover and Text Designer • Trina Stahl

That Patchwork Place® is an imprint of
Martingale & Company™.

The Quilter's Book of Days
Text copyright © 2002 by Carol Endler Sterbenz and authors as
noted.
Photographs copyright © 2002 by Steven Mays and
Martingale & Company as noted.

Martingale & Company
20205 144th Avenue NE
Woodinville, WA 98072-8478 USA
www.martingale-pub.com

Printed in China
07 06 05 04 03 02   8 7 6 5 4 3 2 1

**Library of Congress Cataloging-in-Publication data is
available upon request.**

ISBN 1-56477-454-6

The Quilters: Women and Domestic Art: An Oral History by
Patricia J. Cooper and Norma Bradley Allen, Texas Tech
University Press. Copyright © 1999 by Patricia J. Cooper and
Norma Bradley Allen. Used by permission of Norma Bradley
Allen and Willa Baker.

The Persian Pickle Club by Sandra Dallas. Copyright © 1995 by
Sandra Dallas. Used by permission of St. Martin's Press, LLC.

The Bedquilt by Dorothy Canfield Fisher. Copyright © 1927 by
Dorothy Canfield Fisher. Used by permission of Vivian Scott
Hixson.

Glorious Patchwork by Kaffe Fassett published by Ebury Press.
Copyright © 1997 by Kaffe Fassett. Used by permission of the
Random House Group Ltd.

Passionate Patchwork by Kaffe Fassett published by Ebury Press.
Copyright © 2001 by Kaffe Fassett. Used by permission of the
Random House Group Ltd.

How to Make an American Quilt by Whitney Otto. Copyright
© 1991 by Whitney Otto. Used by permission of Random
House, Inc. and the Joy Harris Literary Agency, Inc.

Quilts among the Plain People by Rachel T. Pellman and Joanne
Ranck. Copyright © 1985 by Rachel T. Pellman and Joanne
Ranck. Used by permission.

How Not to Make a Prize-Winning Quilt by Ami Simms.
Copyright © 1994 by Ami Simms. Used by permission of the
author and Mallery Press.

PHOTOGRAPHS

Jan. 1–7, Feb. 8–14, May 1–7, May 15–21, Aug. 29–31, Sept.
1–7, Sept. 15–21, Oct. 1–7, Nov. 8–14, Sept. 22–28, from *Great
Appliqué: Wonderful Small Quilts.* Copyright © 1994 by Meredith
Corporation. Used by permission.

Jan. 8–14, Feb. 1–7, Apr. 1–7, June 1–7, June 22–28, Aug.
15–21, from *Great Finishes: Patterns and Techniques for Quilting.*
Copyright © 1995 by Meredith Corporation. Used by permission.

May 22–28, from *Decorating with Wreaths, Garlands, Topiaries and
Bouquets* by Carol Endler Sterbenz. Copyright © 1993 by
Rizzoli International Publications, Inc. Text copyright © 1993
by Carol Endler Sterbenz, photography © 1993 by Steven
Mays. Used by permission.

June 8–14, June 29–30, July 1–14, Sept. 8–14, Sept. 29–30, from
Great Patchwork: Stars and Stripes. Copyright © 1994 by
Meredith Corporation. Used by permission.

Jan. 22–28, Mar. 8–14, Apr. 8–14, July 15–21, Nov. 22–28, from
Great Patchwork: Working with Squares and Rectangles. Copyright
© 1995 by Meredith Corporation. Used by permission.

Mar. 15–21, Apr. 29–30, May 8–14, June 15–21, July 22–31,
from *Great Patchwork: Working with Triangles.* Copyright © 1994
by Meredith Corporation. Used by permission.

Jan. 15–21, Apr. 22–28, Aug. 8–14, Oct. 29–31, Nov. 29–30, Dec.
15–28, bibliography, photography by Brent Kane. Copyright ©
1994 by Martingale & Company, That Patchwork Place.

Mar. 29–31, photography by Fred Milke, Jr. Copyright © 1994
by Martingale & Company, That Patchwork Place.

May 29–31, photography by Doug Plager. Copyright © 1994 by
Martingale & Company, That Patchwork Place.

Aug. 1–7, photography by Carl Murray. Copyright © 1994 by
Martingale & Company, That Patchwork Place.

DEDICATION

For John, Bean, Ra, and Gibbies
I am certain of nothing but the holiness of the Heart's affections and the truth of Imagination.
—JOHN KEATS

ACKNOWLEDGMENTS

I am grateful to the many people who contributed to the creation of the book you now hold in your hands. I would like to express my sincerest thanks to: the quilters and designers for carrying the quilting tradition in their hands and in their hearts and whose beautiful quilts form the centerpiece of this work; and to Steven Mays, photographer and dear friend, for giving so generously of his time and talent, and whose work illuminates the pages of this book. My thanks are extended also to the exceptional editors and staff at Martingale & Company who understood my vision and who truly live up to their mission statement to inspire creativity and to enrich the lives they touch, especially to: Jane Hamada, Publisher, for her professional support and friendship, and for leading me to Mary V. Green, Editorial Director extraordinaire; to Tina Cook and Allison Merrill, who shaped the manuscript with sensitivity; to Terry Martin, for her indispensable assistance; to Brent Kane, photographer, who provided the finishing touches, and to Trina Stahl for manifesting the vision in a beautiful design that communicates the heart and soul of the quilter.

FOREWORD

THE THREADS AND patches that form the quilts we sew are the substance of our life stories. While, most often, our quilts are intended for others—to bundle up babies, to protect and comfort family, and to welcome and warm friends whether sleeping, dreaming, or waking—we know that our quilts also contain the rich emotional experiences of the times spent working on them and the gifts that come from having done so. Quilts hold our spirits and connect us to them. It is a connection we seek with a passion.

In *The Quilter's Book of Days*, that connection is celebrated and brought to life in pictures and notations that reveal and illuminate the quilter's world. Organized by week, *The Quilter's Book of Days* is a calendar of priorities and remembrances, lavishly illustrated with full-color photographs of quilts in intimate home settings accompanied by words of inspiration and wisdom for and by the quilter.

J ANUARY

1 NEW YEAR'S DAY
2
3
4
5
6
7

In creating, the only hard thing's to begin; a grass-blade's no easier to make than an oak.

JAMES RUSSELL LOWELL,
A Fable for Critics

8
9
10
11
12
13
14

Sometimes the neighbor women would come in and quilt with Mama. . . . I wanted to keep some of the pretty, bright-colored quilts but Mama would say that we could make do with what we had. Others needed them more.

From *The Quilters*
by PATRICIA COOPER
and NORMA BRADLEY ALLEN

15

16

17

18

19

20

21

Think of music as you orchestrate the shades and patterns; pretend that you are a conductor in a lush symphony hall, imagine the audience saying Ooh *and* Ahh *as they applaud your work.*

WHITNEY OTTO,
How to Make an American Quilt

22
23
24
25
26
27
28

She never knew how her great idea came to her. Sometimes she thought she must have dreamed it. . . . It was too great, too ambitious, too lofty a project for her humble mind to have conceived. Even when she finished drawing the design with her own fingers, she gazed at it incredulously.

DOROTHY CANFIELD FISHER,
"The Bedquilt," from _The Bedquilt and Other Stories_

Making a quilt takes time. Expect that. You'll make mistakes. Expect that, too. Not a day goes by that I don't use a seam ripper.

SANDY BONSIB,
Folk Art Quilts: A Fresh Look

29
30
31

Quilters never question the view that it is perfectly normal to purchase lengths of fabric so that they can cut them up in smaller pieces, only to sew them back together again.

CAROL ENDLER STERBENZ

FEBRUARY

The Amish admire and
enjoy lovely objects because
of their usefulness, regarding
beauty with caution only when
it is connected to pride.

RACHEL THOMAS PELLMAN,
Amish Wall Quilts

1

2

3

4

5

6

7

8

9

10

11

12

13

14
VALENTINE'S DAY

Any quilter who sews a heart pattern in a quilt not meant for a bride is said to be inviting heartache.

QUILTING LORE

15

16

17

18

19

20

21

Support other quilters....
When you let someone know
that you like something they do,
it gives them the confidence
to do more.

SANDY BONSIB,
Folk Art Quilts: A Fresh Look

22
23
24
25
26
27
28/29

Ultimately, the only judge and jury of your work should be your heart.

CAROL ENDLER STERBENZ

Two of the most important things to remember when selecting colors are to have courage and take risks. . . . A quilt becomes a great quilt when something unexpected happens.

MAAIKE BAKKER,
Cups and Saucers

1
2
3
4
5
6
7

MARCH

8

9

10

11

12

13

14

I thought if I invested the time and energy to make a quilt, I'd be more inclined to make the bed. . . . This actually did work—for about two weeks.

AMI SIMMS,
How Not to Make a Prize-Winning Quilt

15

16

17

18

19

20

21

I never knew how a woman with hands as big as chicken hawks could make such neat stitches.

SANDRA DALLAS,
The Persian Pickle Club

Our "simple joys of quilting" are best described as pattern and rhythm, color and value, creation and expression, friendship and sharing.

JOAN HANSON AND MARY HICKEY,
The Simple Joys of Quilting

22
23
24
25
26
27
28

# MARCH

29

30

31

When perfectionism beguiles you, ignore it;
if encouraged, it will be the greatest obstacle to your beginning your work.

JORGEN G. ENDLER

*Quiltmaking cracks open
the door to the future and
allows us to think ahead to our
dreams for our descendants. . . .
A quilt says, "I was here. I
loved you before you even
existed."*

JOAN HANSON AND MARY HICKEY,
The Simple Joys of Quilting

1

2

3

4

5

6

7

$\mathcal{A}$ PRIL

8
9
10
11
12
13
14

$\mathcal{B}$lue color is everlastingly appointed by the Deity to be a source of delight.

JOHN RUSKIN,
Lectures on Architecture and Painting

APRIL

15

16

17

18

19

20

21

The first dream under a new quilt will come true.

QUILTING LORE

$\mathcal{A}$PRIL

22
23
24
25
26
27
28

$\mathcal{A}$lways document your quilt so that the next generation of guardians will know something about you and your history.

CAROL ENDLER STERBENZ

29
30

It is not knowing what will happen until we try a certain combination that makes the process so exciting when it works. Not only works, but sparks, making each of the patterns livelier and more handsome in their relating.

KAFFE FASSETT WITH LIZA PRIOR LUCY,
Glorious Patchwork

While I stood there with a sandwich in one hand, didn't the head of the hull concern come in . . . and pin a big bow of blue ribbon right in the middle of the quilt with a label on it, "First Prize."

DOROTHY CANFIELD FISHER, "The Bedquilt," from *The Bedquilt and Other Stories*

1
2
3
4
5
6
7

A Y

8	
9	
10	
11	
12	
13	
14	

Mehetabel rushed back up the steep attic stairs to her room, and in a joyful agitation began preparations for the work of her life. . . . By some heaven-sent inspiration she had invented a pattern beyond which no patchwork quilt could go.

DOROTHY CANFIELD FISHER,
"The Bedquilt," from *The Bedquilt and Other Stories*

| 15 |
| 16 |
| 17 |
| 18 |
| 19 |
| 20 |
| 21 |

Have nothing in your houses that you do not know to be useful, or believe to be beautiful.

WILLIAM MORRIS,
The Beauty of Life

22

23

24

25

26

27

28

Some people say they don't have an imagination. If you can fantasize about winning the lottery, building your ultimate studio, or traveling around the world and stopping at every fabric shop for souvenirs, then you've got imagination.

ANDREA BALOSKY,
Transitions: Unlocking the Creative Quilter Within

29
30
31

'Tis very warm weather
when one's in bed.

JONATHAN SWIFT,
Journal to Stella

Inspiration: *A heavenly collision of desire,*
talent, and imagination.

CAROL ENDLER STERBENZ

JUNE

	1
	2
	3
	4
	5
	6
	7

If you haven't got the time to do it right, when will you find the time to do it over?

JEFFREY J. MAYER

JUNE

8

9

10

11

12

13

14

Save your opinions for your quilt. Put your heart and voice into it. Cast your ballot; express your feelings regarding . . . emancipation, women's suffrage, your love of family.

WHITNEY OTTO,
How to Make an American Quilt

UNE

15
16
17
18
19
20
21

She took her place by the little table and put the thimble on her knotted, hard finger with the solemnity of a priestess performing a rite.

DOROTHY CANFIELD FISHER,
"The Bedquilt," from *The Bedquilt and Other Stories*

22

23

24

25

26

27

28

*When I make a mistake,
I try to work with it. It's often
the mistakes that I've corrected
that give a quilt its uniqueness,
its character.*

SANDY BONSIB,
Flannel Quilts

29

30

One inexperienced quilter I know made a quilt for her first grandchild,

and it was among the most beautiful quilts I have ever seen.

The corners of the blocks did not quite match, the seams wobbled,

and the quilting was nearly invisible (which was fortunate), but the love and joy

and hope she had for her son's little daughter shone through every stitch.

ROBIN STROBEL, *The Casual Quilter*

 U L Y

1
2
3
4
5
6
7

It's a sight, that big old long-legged man with his boot toes turned in to make a lap to do his piecework on. We've got a fair long road from the highway and three loud dogs out there. They all always sound off when somebody turns up our road. . . . He can git rid of that work quicker than a gnat can bat an eye, when them dogs commence to barkin'.

From *The Quilters*
by PATRICIA COOPER
AND NORMA BRADLEY ALLEN

JULY

8	
9	
10	
11	
12	
13	
14	

I find it very nerve-wracking to have too much help with design and color choices. Not only do people make suggestions, but they expect you to follow them.

MARY HICKEY,
from *The Simple Joys of Quilting*
by Mary Hickey and Joan Hanson

15

16

17

18

19

20

21

Sometimes in quiltmaking, we go off on learning tangents for years. It's no different from real life. Sometimes it takes a long time to learn something simple.

JOAN COLVIN,
The Nature of Design

22
23
24
25
26
27
28

I never get tired of looking at my fabric. It's like looking at a beautiful garden that never goes to seed.

NANCY K. JOHNSON

29
30
31

*I*nstead of throwing unfinished work into the proverbial cupboard

every time you meet a problem, use your seam ripper and try again. Even if

you are unable to solve it completely, the next time you reach the same point,

you will be able to deal with it more successfully and move on.

The sense of achievement more than compensates for the struggle.

DEIRDRE AMSDEN,
Colourwash Quilts

Us little ones had to keep their needles threaded. We'd be out in the yard playin' and they'd holler they needed some needles. We had a whole bunch of needles that we'd run in and thread and stick 'em on top of the quilt for them.

From *The Quilters*
by PATRICIA COOPER
AND NORMA BRADLEY ALLEN

1

2

3

4

5

6

7

AUGUST

8	
9	
10	
11	
12	
13	
14	

A good idea will keep you awake during the morning, but a great idea will keep you awake during the night.

MARILYN VOS SAVANT

| 15 |
| 16 |
| 17 |
| 18 |
| 19 |
| 20 |
| 21 |

No one puts a piece of unshrunk cloth on an old garment, for the patch tears away from the garment, and a worse tear is made.

MATTHEW 9:16
(Revised Standard Version)

22

23

24

25

26

27

28

My quilts track the seasons. In the spring, I take out my cotton quilts. I love them. Then, when the weather gets colder, I put them away and bring out the heavier quilts.

MYRA CROWELL

29
30
31

Quilting is like going into a soundproof room
where the only furniture are the thoughts in my own mind.

CAROL ENDLER STERBENZ

Something special, even magical, happens when you begin to quilt. Smooth fabrics take on intriguing texture, motifs stand out in crisp relief, and graceful patterns swirl across blocks with no regard for piecing boundaries. Quilting is a process, a stitch-by-stitch transformation of fabric and batting into something difficult to describe and pleasing to behold.

Lee Cleland,
Quilting Makes the Quilt

1

2

3

4

5

6

7

$\mathscr{S}$ EPTEMBER

8
9
10
11
12
13
14

$\mathscr{H}$ome is the fragrance of cotton sheets dried in fresh air, the simple charm of polished floors, the heft of handmade quilts lifted from a cedar chest on the first cold night in fall.

CAROL ENDLER STERBENZ,
"Editorial," *Handcraft Illustrated,*
November/December 1993

What is this magical textile known as a quilt? . . . A quilt is a work of art that brings color and comfort into our lives. As it hangs on a wall, it softens the environment, absorbing echoes and noise. As it covers our bodies in slumber, it brings warmth, comfort, and a flood of memories that lull us into serenity.

NANCY J. MARTIN,
Make Room for Quilts

15

16

17

18

19

20

21

September

22
23
24
25
26
27
28

The happiness of life is made up of minute fractions—the little soon forgotten charities of a kiss or smile, a kind look, a heartfelt compliment, and the countless infinitesimals of pleasurable and genial feeling.

SAMUEL TAYLOR COLERIDGE,
The Improvisatore

29
30

Creativity is like climbing an uneven staircase.

Sometimes you ascend with ease, but at other times you seem to stay

on one level so long that you begin to wonder if there are any more steps.

However experienced you become, the staircase remains unpredictable,

which is the very reason that creative activity is so

fascinating, addictive, and exhilarating.

DEIRDRE AMSDEN, *Colourwash Quilts*

OCTOBER

1
2
3
4
5
6
7

It's not that quilting requires all night to accomplish, but there's something deeply reassuring about settling down to work after the house is quiet. It seems like night suddenly dissolves into morning.

CAROL ENDLER STERBENZ

OCTOBER

8
9
10
11
12
13
14

Making a scrap quilt means that I get to play in my stash. I revisit old friends and discover some new ones. I get to find new, exciting color and print combinations. In short, I get to do what I love best— play with fabric.

SALLY SCHNEIDER,
Scrap Frenzy

I wasn't that concerned with corners meeting and seams lying flat. . . . I figured if I shook the top and nothing fell off I was doing pretty good!

AMI SIMMS,
*How Not to Make
a Prize-Winning Quilt*

15
16
17
18
19
20
21

22

23

24

25

26

27

28

Making quilts should be fun. Try to enjoy the process as much as you expect to enjoy the product. Remember that we are not making quilts for the same reasons our grandmothers did. If we don't finish a quilt today, it doesn't mean we'll be cold tonight.

SANDY BONSIB,
Flannel Quilts

29
30
31

$\mathscr{A}$s far back as I can remember, I've been stopped in my tracks by arrangements of humble squares. Stacks of boxes on a shelf, bricks in a building yard, square-cut flint stone walls and aerial views of farmers' fields all make me remember how powerful this simplest of geometric forms can be.

KAFFE FASSETT WITH LIZY PRIOR LUCY,
Passionate Patchwork

November

*Make something by hand—
it will be a dwelling place for
your spirit for all time. And as
you work, know that you are
joining with all before you, and
all who will come after you,
when all that may be left behind
of your walk through life is this
testimony . . . made by your
hands.*

CAROL ENDLER STERBENZ,
"From the Editor," *Handcraft Illustrated*,
Christmas 1997

| 1 |
| 2 |
| 3 |
| 4 |
| 5 |
| 6 |
| 7 |

November

8
9
10
11
12
13
14

My top was perfect . . . but when we flapped it out on the bed it had a belly big enough to hide a cat. . . . There seemed to be large pockets of air trapped underneath. No sooner did we burp one side than the air pockets redistributed to another! . . . Then I heard those immortal words: "Don't worry, it'll quilt out."

AMI SIMMS,
*How Not to Make
a Prize-Winning Quilt*

November

15

16

17

18

19

20

21

I make quilts for babies, not for their parents, and not necessarily to match the decor of their rooms. . . . I want them to be dragged around the house, into the car, and into the yard. If they are bright and busy, they will be noticed, used, and loved.

Ursula Reikes,
Quilts for Baby

November

22

23

24

25

26

27

28

That is the principal thing: not to remain with the dream, with the intention, with the being in the mood, but always forcibly to convert it into all things.

Rainer Maria Rilke

29
30

Always work from your heart. It's fine to be interested in how others respond to your quilts, but you must be true to yourself. Listen to your own voice and follow your vision.

VELDA NEWMAN,
Velda Newman: A Painter's Approach to Quilt Design

A WORLD OF DOLL HOUSES

DECEMBER

I wonder how many people have taken cover under this quilt . . . passed from hand to hand, from family member to family member, and finally to a stranger. I recognize the universality of quilts and take comfort in them.

CAROL ENDLER STERBENZ

1
2
3
4
5
6
7

DECEMBER

8
9
10
11
12
13
14

I have always been delighted at the prospect of a new day, a fresh try, one more start, with perhaps a bit of magic waiting somewhere behind the morning.

J.B. PRIESTLY

DECEMBER

Worrying about doing things the right way when trying to be creative makes taking risks impossible. Right-way thinking says that dogs aren't bigger than houses or that women aren't blue or that the sun doesn't have a big smile on its face. Creative thinking says, "Why not?"

MARY LOU WEIDMAN,
Whimsies and Whynots

15

16

17

18

19

20

21

DECEMBER

22
23
24
25
26
27
28

As I face that blank design wall, I am happy and grateful to be there. If the surface begins to vibrate with unexplored ideas, I am pulled into the design process. If the white space before me stays that way, I can enjoy it as a clean antidote to the clutter of living.

JOAN COLVIN,
The Nature of Design

29

30

31
NEW YEAR'S EVE

$\mathscr{S}$oon it will be fittingly winter, a time when the change of weather

will also cause me to change the kinds of crafts I do.

I will be drawn to projects with more heft, especially quilting,

and I will try again to finish the quilt with the

Dresden plate pattern started years and years ago . . . .

CAROL ENDLER STERBENZ,
"From the Editor," *Handcraft Illustrated*, Winter 1996

BIBLIOGRAPHY

Aldrich, Margret, ed. *This Old Quilt: A Heartwarming Celebration of Quilts and Quilting Memories.* Stillwater, Minn.: Voyageur Press, 2001.

Amsden, Deirdre. *Colourwash Quilts: A Personal Approach to Design and Technique.* Bothell, Wash.: That Patchwork Place, 1994.

Bakker, Maaike. *Cups and Saucers: Paper-Pieced Quilt Designs.* Bothell, Wash.: Martingale & Company, 2000.

Balosky, Andrea. *Transitions: Unlocking the Creative Quilter Within.* Bothell, Wash.: That Patchwork Place, 1996.

Bonsib, Sally. *Folk Art Quilts: A Fresh Look.* Bothell, Wash.: Martingale & Company, 1998.

———. *Flannel Quilts.* Bothell, Wash.: Martingale & Company, 2001.

Cleland, Lee. *Quilting Makes the Quilt.* Bothell, Wash.: That Patchwork Place, 1994.

Colvin, Joan. *The Nature of Design: A Quilt Artist's Personal Journal.* Bothell, Wash.: That Patchwork Place, 1996.

Cook, John, comp. *The Book of Positive Quotations.* Minneapolis: Rubicon Press, Inc., 1993.

Cooper, Patricia, and Norma Bradley Allen. *The Quilters: Women and Domestic Art: An Oral History.* Lubbock, Tex.: Texas Tech University Press, 1999.

Dallas, Sandra. *The Persian Pickle Club.* New York: St. Martin's Griffin, 1995.

Fassett, Kaffe, with Liza Prior Lucy. *Glorious Patchwork.* New York: Clarkson N. Potter, Inc., 1997.

———. *Passionate Patchwork.* Newton, Conn.: The Taunton Press, 2001.

Fisher, Dorothy Canfield. *The Bedquilt and Other Stories.* Ed. Madigan, Mark J. Columbia, Miss.: University of Missouri Press, 1996.

Great Appliqué: Wonderful Small Quilts. Des Moines, Iowa: Better Homes and Gardens, 1994.

Great Finishes: Patterns and Techniques for Quilting. Des Moines, Iowa: Better Homes and Gardens, 1995.

Great Patchwork: Stars and Stripes. Des Moines, Iowa: Better Homes and Gardens, 1994.

Great Patchwork: Working with Squares and Rectangles. Des Moines, Iowa: Better Homes and Gardens, 1995.

Great Patchwork: Working with Triangles. Des Moines, Iowa: Better Homes and Gardens, 1994.

Hanson, Joan and Mary Hickey. *The Simple Joys of Quilting: 30 Timeless Quilt Projects.* Bothell, Wash.: Martingale & Company, 2001.

Holy Bible, Revised Standard Version.

Martin, Nancy J. *Make Room for Quilts.* Bothell, Wash.: That Patchwork Place, 1994.

Newman, Velda, with Christine Barnes. *Velda Newman: A Painter's Approach to Quilt Design.* Bothell, Wash.: That Patchwork Place, 1996.

Otto, Whitney. *How to Make an American Quilt.* New York: Villard Books, 1991.

Pellman, Rachel T., and Joanne Ranck. *Quilts among the Plain People.* Lancaster, Penn.: Good Books, 1981. Cited in Margret Aldrich, ed., *This Old Quilt.*

Pellman, Rachel T. *Amish Wall Quilts.* Bothell, Wash.: Martingale & Company, 2001.

Quotable Women: A Celebration. Philadelphia: Running Press Book Publishers, 2000.

Reikes, Ursula. *Quilts for Baby: Easy as ABC.* Bothell, Wash.: That Patchwork Place, 1993.

Schneider, Sally. *Scrap Frenzy: Even More Quick-Pieced Scrap Quilts.* Bothell, Wash.: Martingale & Company, 2001.

Simms, Ami. *How Not to Make a Prize-Winning Quilt.* Flint, Mich.: Mallery Press, 1994. Cited in Margret Aldrich, ed., *This Old Quilt.*

Sterbenz, Carol Endler. *Decorating with Wreaths, Garlands, Topiaries and Bouquets.* New York: Rizzoli, 1993.

———. "From the Editor," *Handcraft Illustrated.* Boston: Boston Common Press, Christmas 1997.

———. "From the Editor," *Handcraft Illustrated.* Boston: Boston Common Press, November/ December 1993.

———. "From the Editor," *Handcraft Illustrated.* Boston: Boston Common Press, Winter 1996.

Strobel, Robin. *The Casual Quilter: Six Stress-Free Projects.* Bothell, Wash.: Martingale & Company, 2002.

Weidman, Mary Lou. *Whimsies and Whynots.* Bothell, Wash.: That Patchwork Place, 1997.

QUILTMAKERS

Foreword, unknown;

January 1–7, unknown;

January 8–14, Judy Doenias;

January 15–21, from the collection of Felicia Holtzinger;

January 22–28, Frances Calhoun, Judith Doenias, and Jean Perry;

January 29–31, Nancy K. Johnson;

February 1–7, Jeanne Elliott;

February 8–14, Sally Korte and Alice Strebel;

February 15–21, from the collection of Patricia Ann Ellis;

February 22–28/29, unknown;

March 1–7, Mimi Shimmin (pieced and quilted by Caroline Kearney);

March 8–14, unknown;

March 15–21, Jean Hoblitzell;

March 22–28, unknown;

March 29–31, unknown;

April 1–7, Katharine Brainard;

April 8–14, Diane Rode Schneck;

April 15–21, unknown;

April 22–28, from the collection of Felicia Holtzinger;

April 29–30, Aurelie Dwyer Stack (quilted by Marjorie Downs);

May 1–7, Katharine Brainard;

May 8–14, Margaret B. Brehmer;

May 15–21, unknown;

May 22–28, unknown;

June 1–7, Joyce Sullivan;

June 8–14, Suellen Cochrane Wassem;

June 15–21, unknown;

June 22–28, Diane Rode Schneck;

June 29–30, wall hanging at bottom center by Diane Rode Schneck, others unknown;

July 1–7, Sandra Dikordki;

July 8–14, Katharine Brainard;

July 15–21, unknown;

July 22–28, Sharon Wren;

July 29–31, unknown;

August 8–14, Kristen Adams;

August 15–21, unknown;

August 22–28, unknown;

August 29–31, Mimi Shimmin;

September 1–7, unknown;

September 8–14, Katharine Brainard;

September 15–21, Edith Olbrich (quilted by Lillian Olsen);

September 22–28, Jacquelyn Smyth;

September 29–30, unknown;

October 1–7, Polly Whitehorn;

October 8–14, unknown;

October 15–21, unknown;

October 22–28, unknown;

October 29–31, from the collection of Dr. Ray and Elizabeth Robinson;

November 8–14, Sonya Lee Barrington;

November 15–21, unknown;

November 22–28, unknown;

November 29–30, from the collection of Felicia Holtzinger;

December 1–7, unknown;

December 8–14, unknown;

December 15–21, from the collection of Felicia Holtzinger;

December 22–28, Joan Colvin;

December 29–31, Carol Endler Sterbenz.